Boffin Boy and the Moon Zombies
by David Orme

Illustrated by Peter Richardson

Published by Ransom Publishing Ltd.
Unit 7, Brocklands Farm, West Meon, Hants. GU32 1JN
www.ransom.co.uk

ISBN   978 178127 049 3
First published in 2013
Reprinted 2014, 2015
Copyright © 2013 Ransom Publishing Ltd.

Illustrations copyright © 2013 Peter Richardson

A CIP catalogue record of this book is available from the British
Library.

Design & layout: *redpaperdesign.co.uk*

Find out more about Boffin Boy at *www.ransom.co.uk*

Boffin Boy
AND THE
Moon Zombies

By David Orme
Illustrated by Peter Richardson

Back on Earth, the zombies are busy …

So Boffin Boy goes to the Moon ...

ABOUT THE AUTHOR

David Orme has written well over 200 books
including poetry collections, fiction and non-
fiction, and school text books. He especially
likes writing science fiction stories, and historical
stories set in London. Find out more at:
www.magic-nation.com.